Literacy BASICS

FOR AGES 10-11 KEY STAGE 2

Contents

Unstressed vowels

Look and learn

button

celebrate

Sometimes vowels in longer words are **not stressed**, or pronounced. These vowels are often difficult to hear. The words above both contain **unstressed vowels**.

Practice

Fill in the missing unstressed vowels in each word below. Use a dictionary if necessary.

1. env_e_lope

2. b__s__ness

3. comp__ny

4. entr__nce

5. ment__l

6. photogr__pher

7. diction__ry

8. valu__ble

9. secr__t__ry

10. int__rest

11. cem__t__ry

12. trav__l

Challenge

Join up the syllables.   Write the word and underline any unstressed vowels.

dif		nes		y		**1.** _____
Wed		ar		ture		**2.** _____
his		fer		day		**3.** _____
bach		na		ate		**4.** _____
sep		el		ent		**5.** diff<u>e</u>rent _____
sig		tor		or		**6.** _____

Root words

Look and learn

A **root word** is a word to which **prefixes** or **suffixes** may be added.
Sometimes the root word is **easy** to see. Sometimes the root word is **harder** to work out.

unhelpful (root word – help)

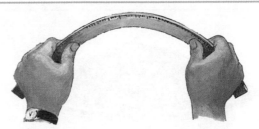

flexibility (root word – flexible)

Practice

Find and write the root word of each longer word below.

1.	bicycle	_cycle_	**2.**	triangle	_____
3.	exported	_____	**4.**	injustice	_____
5.	friendliness	_____	**6.**	uncontrollable	_____
7.	admission	_____	**8.**	magically	_____
9.	disagreement	_____	**10.**	signature	_____
11.	competition	_____	**12.**	proposal	_____
13.	generously	_____			
14.	unsuitable	_____			
15.	sympathise	_____			

Challenge

Add prefixes and suffixes. Make at least two longer words from each root word.

root word	longer words
appear	disappear, appearing
cover	
like	
comfort	
colour	
weak	

3

Dashes and brackets

Look and learn

A **dash** holds words apart. It is stronger than a comma. It is not as strong as a full stop.

Brackets enclose information to show it is separate from the rest of the sentence.

Sam ordered his favourite meal – curry.

The Pyramids (found in Egypt) are huge.

Practice

Choose the best ending to complete each sentence.

Sentence endings
a marvellous invention.
or you'll be in trouble.
she had pink hair.
all green and slimy.
football!
my old teddy.
Treasure Island.
I hate it!
for painting a picture.
a silver one.

1. There is only one sport worth playing – <u>football!</u>

2. My sister loves pop music – _____

3. John Logie Baird invented television – _____

4. I have got a mountain bike – _____

5. One girl was different – _____

6. I read a great book last week – _____

7. Get your homework in on time – _____

8. Tom won a competition – _____

9. The monster appeared – _____

10. In the attic I found an old friend – _____

Challenge

Choose the best "filling" to go inside each pair of brackets.

| over 26 miles | a red sports car | in Africa | a famous composer | 1666 |

1. The Great Fire of London (_____) was terrible.

2. Mount Kilimanjaro (_____) always has snow at the top.

3. Beethoven (_____) wrote lots of music.

4. Each year there is a marathon (_____) in New York.

5. The man parked his car (_____).

Look and learn

Words may be divided into groups called **parts of speech**. Three important parts of speech are: **nouns**, **verbs** and **adjectives**.

This is a **noun**. It is a **naming word**.

The happy lady was laughing.

This is an **adjective**. It is a **describing word**. It tells us more about the **noun**.

This is a **verb**. It is a word that describes **actions**.

Practice

In the following sentences:
circle the adjectives; tick the nouns; underline the verbs.

1. I tripped over the uneven floor.

2. The silly boy crashed his new bike.

3. When the old lady reached her house, she sat down.

4. We saw wild horses in the forest.

5. The large crowd cheered as the skilful player scored.

6. The giggling girls annoyed the teacher.

7. A prickly hedgehog snuffled in the dry leaves.

8. The lazy man was sleeping under the tall tree.

Challenge

Think of a suitable word for each gap. In the brackets write if it is a noun, verb or adjective.

1. Sam put the _____ suitcase on the floor.   (_____)

2. Athens is the capital of _____.   (_____)

3. The mountaineers _____ to the summit.   (_____)

4. The children sang loudly at the _____.   (_____)

5. The cat's _____ was soft and silky.   (_____)

6. The helicopter _____ over the motorway.   (_____)

Connectives

We sometimes join two **clauses** together by using a **connective**.

Sam is good at swimming   because   he practices a lot.

| clause 1 | connective | clause 2 |

Practice

Choose the best connective to join each pair of sentences.

Connectives

1. I turned on the tap _____so that_____ I could have a drink.   (so that/as)
2. The helicopter flew near the volcano _____ it erupted.   (where/when)
3. I know a man _____ has seven cats.   (which/who)
4. I visit my grandmother _____ I have time.   (that/whenever)
5. Anna stopped blowing up the balloon _____ it burst.   (so/in case)
6. Tom pumped up his tyre _____ he wouldn't get a puncture. (until/so that)
7. The Middle East is important _____ it has lots of oil.   (during/as)
8. I always do my homework _____ I watch TV.   (although/before)
9. The children were running _____ they were late.   (if/because)
10. The cat chased the mouse _____ it came out of the hole.   (since/when)

Challenge

Think of a good clause to complete each sentence.

1. I ran until _____ .
2. The children quietened down when _____ .
3. Alice found a key that _____ .
4. Tom fell off the wall on which _____ .
5. Lucy was a girl who _____ .

Prefixes and suffixes

Look and learn

We add **prefixes** and **suffixes** to words to **change their meanings**.

happy – **un**happy

A **prefix** is added to the **beginning** of a word. It **does not** change the spelling of the root word.

empty – empti**ness**

A **suffix** is added to the **end** of a word. It may **sometimes** change the spelling of the root word.

Practice

Choose the correct prefix to complete each word.

1. _bi_ cycle (con/bi)
2. _____ merge (sub/tele)
3. _____ plane (in/aero)

4. _____ mature (in/im)
5. _____ considerate (in/im)
6. _____ responsible (ex/ir)

7. _____ angle (tri/micro)
8. _____ legal (ex/il)
9. _____ fix (pre/de)

10. _____ face (mis/de)
11. _____ understand (dis/mis)
12. _____ fill (dis/re)

13. _____ metre (centi/aqua)
14. _____ clockwise (anti/mal)
15. _____ change (for/ex)

Challenge

Take the suffix off each word. Write the root word.

1. babies   baby
2. nastiness   _____

3. beautiful   _____
4. quarrelling   _____

5. shiny   _____
6. operation   _____

7. knives   _____
8. microscopic   _____

9. burglar   _____
10. mysterious   _____

11. attendance   _____
12. excitable   _____

Active and passive verbs

Look and learn

The thief **stole** the jewels.

| A verb is **active** when the subject of the sentence does the action. |

The jewels **were stolen** by the thief.

| A verb is **passive** when the subject of the sentence has the action done to it. |

Practice

Underline the verb in the each sentence. Say if it is active (A) or passive (P).

1. The lion <u>chased</u> the deer. (A)   2. The car was driven by the lady. (___)

3. The author wrote lots of books. (___)   4. The doctor listened to my heart. (___)

5. The cup was won by the girls. (___)   6. The tree was chopped down by the man. (___)

7. The river ran through the valley. (___)   8. The candle was blown out by the wind. (___)

9. The child bought some sweets. (___)   10. The avalanche crashed down the mountain. (___)

11. The goal was scored by Jess. (___)   12. The dog chased the cat. (___)

Challenge

Rewrite each sentence. Change the verb from passive to active.

1. The car was stopped by the police officer.   <u>The police officer stopped the car.</u>

2. My luggage was carried by a porter. _____

3. The mouse was chased by the cat. _____

4. The gold medal was won by the relay team. _____

5. The coin was picked up by the boy. _____

6. The window was broken by the girl. _____

7. The glass was dropped by Sam. _____

8. The carrot was eaten by the horse. _____

9. All the keys were stolen by the thief. _____

10. Ben was hugged by his aunt. _____

Where do our words come from?

Look and learn

English is not just **one language**. It is made up of words taken from many **other languages**.

spaghetti
| Italy |

jungle
| India |

ballet
| France |

yacht
| Holland |

Practice

Fill in each gap with a word from the Word Box.

Here are some words that come from France.

Word Box	
duvet	banquet
ballet	buffet
bracket	cabaret
trumpet	sachet
scarlet	ricochet
bouquet	blanket

1. _____Scarlet_____ is a dark red colour.
2. A _____ holds up a shelf.
3. A _____ is a bunch of flowers.
4. A _____ is a small packet.
5. A _____ is a musical instrument.
6. A _____ is a bed covering, filled with feathers.
7. A _____ is a number of different acts.
8. _____ is a kind of dance.
9. A _____ is a special feast.
10. A _____ is a bed covering.
11. A _____ is a meal where you serve yourself.
12. A _____ is when something hits a surface and bounces off.

Challenge

Use a dictionary to help you. Decide which country each word comes from.

Word	Country of origin
1. pizza	
2. schooner	
3. café	
4. kangaroo	
5. wok	
6. moccasins	
7. bungalow	
8. reggae	

There is a word from each of these countries: France, America, Jamaica, China, Italy, India, Australia, Holland.

Mnemonics

Look and learn

A **mnemonic** is a way of remembering the spelling of tricky words.

An island **is land** surrounded by water.

Practice

Which words do these clues help you to solve?

favourite	
piece	
believe	
business	
weight	
young	
bicycle	
miserable	
separate	
conscience	

1. Catch a **bus in** to your ___business___ .
2. _____ has a **rat in** it.
3. _____ is **our** best word.
4. Don't ride your _____ in **icy** weather.
5. _____ has **science** in it.
6. I would like a _____ of **pie**.
7. **You** are only _____ once.
8. Never _____ a **lie**.
9. A **miser** is always _____ .
10. What's the _____ of **eight** people?

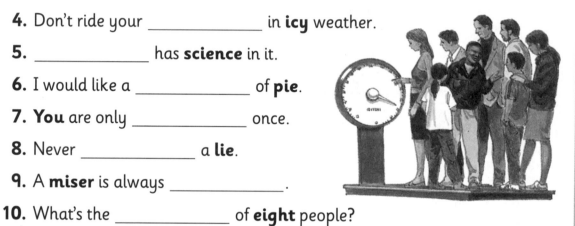

Challenge

Underline the tricky bit in each word. Make up your own mnemonic to help you spell each word.

1. temperature _____
2. skeleton _____
3. vegetable _____
4. cupboard _____
5. sword _____
6. restaurant _____
7. marriage _____
8. headache _____
9. friend _____
10. chocolate _____

Punctuation

Look and learn

Punctuation helps us to make sense of what we read. **Punctuation marks** make writing easier for us to understand. They can make a lot of difference!

The soldier entered on his head, a helmet on each foot, a sandal in his hand. He had his trusty sword.

 ✗

The soldier entered. On his head a helmet, on each foot a sandal. In his hand he had his trusty sword.

✓

Practice

Rewrite each sentence. Punctuate it correctly.

1. the man asked is it raining _____
2. Ive lost my pen rohan shouted _____
3. the burglar whispered someones coming _____
4. wheres my bag mrs shah asked _____
5. you will need a pen a ruler and some paper _____
6. the noise a loud banging noise was awful _____
7. the childrens clothes were on the floor _____
8. what a lovely surprise the teacher said _____
9. pass the salt please sams dad asked _____
10. the boys coat was torn _____

Challenge

Rewrite this sign. Make it mean the opposite by changing only the puntuation marks.

DANGER.

NO SWIMMING ALLOWED.

Look and learn

The English language has been influenced by **many other languages**. Understanding the **origins** of words sometimes helps us spell them.

In Latin 'signum' means 'a sign'.

From the word 'signum' we get the words 'signal' and 'signature'.

Practice

Complete the chart correctly with words from the Word Box.

	Latin word	Meaning	English words
1.	signum	a sign	signal, signature
2.	scribere	to write	
3.	videre	to see	
4.	pedum	foot	
5.	gratus	pleasing	
6.	specare	to look	
7.	liber	free	
8.	civis	citizen	

Word Box	
describe	pedal
congratulate	vision
spectator	signal
evident	liberty
liberal	grateful
signature	city
civilian	pedestrian
spectacles	scribble

Challenge

Complete the chart with some words you think might come from these Greek words:

	Greek word	Meaning	English words
1.	phone	sound	telephone, microphone
2.	geo	earth	
3.	auto	self	
4.	graph	to write	
5.	aster	a star	
6.	scope	I see	

Complex sentences

Look and learn

Alice found a key   which opened the door.

main clause   subordinate clause

Many complex sentences are made up of a **main clause**
and a **subordinate clause** (a less important clause).

Practice

Join up each main clause from Set A with an appropriate subordinate clause from Set B.

Set A

1. The children began to shout
2. Last night I read a good book
3. Alexander Bell was the inventor
4. I visited Athens
5. I collect stamps
6. Samuel Pepys lived in London

Set B

when I went to bed.
which is in Greece.
because they are so colourful.
when the teacher left the room.
during the Great Fire in 1666.
who invented the telephone.

Write the sentences you have made:

1. _____
2. _____
3. _____
4. _____
5. _____
6. _____

Challenge

Think of a suitable subordinate clause to finish each complex sentence:

1. I like cats because _____.

2. My pet rabbit escaped when _____.

3. I climbed the tree so that _____.

4. I saw the queen when _____.

5. The explorer kept walking until _____.

6. The snake slithered through the grass just as _____.

Look and learn

Look before you leap.

A proverb is a **wise saying** that has been around a **long time**.

Practice

Choose the best word to complete each proverb.

never	clean	worm	cooks	one
nine	speed	well	birds	served

1. Too many ___cooks___ spoil the broth.
2. More haste, less _____.
3. First come, first _____.
4. Better late than _____.
5. If a job is worth doing, it's worth doing _____.
6. New brooms sweep _____.
7. A stitch in time saves _____.
8. Two heads are better than _____.
9. The early bird catches the _____.
10. _____ of a feather flock together.

Challenge

Finish each of these proverbs:

1. Every cloud _____.
2. Empty vessels _____.
3. Don't put all your eggs _____.
4. Still waters _____.
5. One good turn _____.
6. A rolling stone _____.
7. Great minds _____.
8. Out of the frying pan _____.

Syllables

Look and learn

par – a – chute (3 syllables)

Words can be broken down into smaller parts, called **syllables**.

Practice

Work out these syllable 'sums'.

1. de + ter + mine = <u>determine</u>

2. um + brel + la = _____

3. con + fid + ent = _____

4. e + lec + tric = _____

5. in + fec + ted = _____

6. in + tro + duce = _____

7. chat + ter + box = _____

8. hos + pit + al = _____

9. rest + less + ness = _____

10. re + mem + ber = _____

11. dif + fer + ent = _____

12. Jan + u + ar + y = _____

13. at + ten + tion = _____

14. u + ni + form = _____

15. con + duc + tor = _____

Challenge

Think of a suitable second syllable for each word. Then write the whole word.

1. ac + <u>ro</u> + bat = <u>acrobat</u>

2. Nov + _____ + ber = _____

3. pro + _____ + al = _____

4. help + _____ + ly = _____

5. ad + _____ + ture = _____

6. lem + _____ + ade = _____

7. ex + _____ + lent = _____

8. dis + _____ + er = _____

9. con + _____ + ent = _____

10. ex + _____ + sive = _____

Using dictionaries

Look and learn

> **lubricate**
> to oil or grease the moving parts of a machine so they run smoothly.

You can use a dictionary to find the **meaning** of a word and to check its **spelling**.

Practice

Use a dictionary to help you solve these clues. They are in alphabetical order.

1. A_crobat_ Someone who does balancing tricks.
2. B_____ Lovely – very pretty.
3. C_____ Stops wine coming out of a bottle.
4. D_____ Not safe – risky.
5. E_____ Costs a lot.
6. F_____ A shallow river crossing.
7. G_____ A quick look.
8. H_____ A six-sided shape.
9. I_____ A pointed stick of ice.
10. J_____ Make fun of person in rude way.
11. K_____ A sharp cutting tool.
12. L_____ A long spear carried by knights.
13. M_____ Something worn over the face.
14. N_____ Not wide.
15. O_____ A sea creature with tentacles.
16. P_____ Quiet and calm.
17. Q_____ Where ships moor.
18. R_____ Not long ago.
19. S_____ Rare.
20. T_____ A shop assistant puts money in it.
21. U_____ To join together.
22. V_____ Not clear.
23. W_____ Clever and amusing.
24. X_____ A short form of Christmas.
25. Y_____ A type of sailing boat.
26. Z_____ To move or climb suddenly.

Challenge

Spell these words correctly. Use a dictionary to help.

1. calender _____calendar_____
2. resevoir _____
3. parliment _____
4. goverment _____
5. delicous _____
6. dissappear _____
7. somersalt _____
8. alltogether _____
9. sissors _____
10. kangeroo _____

Spelling rules

Look and learn

Some **spelling rules** are helpful to remember. One of the more commonly quoted rules is:

i (when it makes the sound **ee**) before **e** except after **c**

I bel**ie**ve the th**ie**f stole a p**ie**ce of cake.

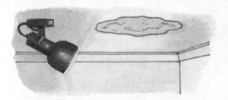

The pancake is on the c**ei**ling!

Practice

Make these words.

ie

1. ach___ve
   achieve
2. bel___ve
   _____
3. br___f
   _____
4. ch___f
   _____
5. f___ld
   _____

ie

6. sh___ld
   _____
7. p___ce
   _____
8. s___ge
   _____
9. bab___s
   _____
10. cop___s
    _____

ei

11. c___ling
    _____
12. rec___ve
    _____
13. dec___ve
    _____
14. perc___ve
    _____
15. conc___t
    _____

Challenge

Follow the rule! Choose **ie** or **ei**. Check in a dictionary if you are not sure.

1. pr___st
2. misch___f
3. dec___t
4. rel___f
5. c___ling
6. n___ce
7. shr___k
8. s___ve
9. conc___ted
10. y___ld
11. rec___ve
12. f___rce

NB: There are some words which don't stick to the rules!

seize

weird

forfeit

Look and learn

A **conditional verb** tells you the action **might** happen (or might have happened), because it **depends** on someone or something else.

I **would** go out if it stopped raining.

I **could** not eat the apple because it was bad.

Practice

Match up the beginnings and endings of these sentences. Circle the conditional verb in each.

1. If the snow continues		you should have a drink.
2. If you are thirsty		if I keep putting money in this machine.
3. If I had the money		I would cut everyone's taxes.
4. I could have swum across the river		we (might) get cut off.
5. I might win the jackpot		until we had finished our work.
6. She would have passed the test		but there were too many crocodiles.
7. The teacher would not let us go home		they would be able to fly!
8. I told you if you shouted		I would buy a new pair of trainers.
9. If I were the Prime Minister		you would wake the baby.
10. If cows had wings		but she didn't practise enough.

Challenge

Complete the conditional sentences with suitable endings.

1. I would like _____.

2. Would you _____.

3. If she pushes me again _____.

4. If I win the Lottery _____.

5. I might go to the party if _____.

6. If only I had worked harder _____.

7. If I had not overslept _____.

8. No one would notice if _____.

Shortening sentences

Look and learn

We can **shorten** sentences by taking out adjectives and adverbs (describing words).

The tired old man slowly sat down.
The man sat down.

When we write **notes** we only write down **essential** words.

Dinner in oven

This actually means:
I have put your dinner in the oven to keep it hot.

Practice

Shorten these sentences. Cross out the adjectives and adverbs.

1. The small, black dog noisily barked at the tall man.
2. The pink-haired lady shouted angrily at the young waiter.
3. The fat, bearded man easily lifted his heavy sack.
4. My favourite footballer skilfully scored a beautiful goal.
5. Whizzo, the jolly clown, fell awkwardly off the stepladder.
6. Gary Goldberg, the famous singer, silently slipped out of the back door.
7. Our new car was badly damaged in the accident.
8. The chattering monkeys noisily climbed up the swaying tree.
9. The glamorous lady waited eagerly for her handsome husband.
10. My best friend quickly answered the door.

Challenge

Convert these notes into proper sentences, punctuated correctly.

Jaguars like water — good swimmers — live near rivers — catch turtles and fish — female jaguars teach young — stay with mothers for two years.

_____

_____

_____

_____

_____

Look and learn

Why runnest thou hither and thither?

Many **words** and **expressions** have **changed**.

The **astronauts** prepared for **countdown**.

New words enter our language all the time.

Practice

Match up the old and new version of the words and phrases.

1.	wilt	lives
2.	saith	truly
3.	abides	will
4.	ye	look at
5.	verily	says
6.	wondrous	are
7.	behold	wonderful
8.	art	you

9.	over yonder	Do as you are told.
10.	hither and thither	What do you want?
11.	Do as thou art bidden.	Who lives here?
12.	to tarry awhile	over there
13.	What dost thou desire?	Are you a friend or an enemy?
14.	Art thou friend or foe?	Come here.
15.	Who abides within?	to stay for a while
16.	Come nigh.	here and there

Challenge

Tick which of these words you think have entered our language in the last 50 years.

mobile phone ✓	pen	television	
	farm	computer	satellite
wheelie	house	video	
	calculator	dinosaur	cheeseburger
mill	sneaker	trainers	
	floppy disk	chimney	motel
wood	Internet	astronaut	

Formal language

Look and learn

Keep quiet!

We speak to each other **informally**.

You are forbidden to engage in conversation.

OFFICIAL NOTICE

Official language is very **formal**.

Practice

Match up these formal and informal ways of saying things.

1. Can you decipher my writing?
2. Kindly append your signature.
3. Many thanks for your donation.
4. I regret I am unable to attend.
5. Please reply to my correspondence.
6. I bid you farewell.
7. Please desist from walking on the grass.
8. Apologies for any inconvenience caused.
9. Do not hinder my progress.
10. Kindly settle your debt immediately.

Thanks for the gift.

Please answer my letter.

Keep off the grass.

Get out of my way.

Can you read my writing?

Pay up at once.

Sorry I can't come.

Cheerio.

Sorry to have bothered you.

Please sign this.

Challenge

Write what you think these formal notices mean.

1. Thieves will be prosecuted.

2. Vehicular travel prohibited.

3. You are requested not to consume your food on these premises.

4. Concealing information is a punishable offence.

5. Kindly register on entry.

6. The management cannot accept any liability for theft.

Changing words

Look and learn

We can often change a **root word** by adding a **prefix**.

zzkflmpjx!

My name is Luke.

We can often change a **root word** by adding a **suffix**.

nonsense ← sense → sensible

(root word + prefix)　　(root word)　　(root word + suffix)

Practice

Choose a prefix from the box to complete each word.

1. __mid__ air
2. _____ stand
3. _____ cast
4. _____ current
5. _____ friend
6. _____ behave
7. _____ code
8. _____ face
9. _____ grade
10. _____ approve
11. _____ bid
12. _____ sphere
13. _____ plant
14. _____ ordinary
15. _____ marine

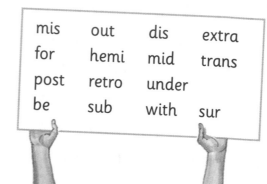

mis	out	dis	extra
for	hemi	mid	trans
post	retro	under	
be	sub	with	sur

Challenge

Take the suffix off each word. Write the root word correctly.

1. historian ___history___
2. beggar _____
3. observatory _____
4. reception _____
5. president _____
6. kingdom _____
7. argument _____
8. cowardice _____
9. magnetism _____
10. friendship _____
11. apologise _____
12. sparkle _____
13. simplify _____
14. cyclist _____

More about complex sentences

Look and learn

The chips were cold | when I ate them.

main clause | subordinate clause

A **complex** sentence contains a **main clause** and a **subordinate** (less important) **clause**. The subordinate clause may not make sense on its own.

Practice

Circle the main clause and underline the subordinate clause in each sentence.

1. The wind was so cold that I put on a coat.
2. The dog dug a hole for his bone so he could bury it.
3. When I am eighteen, I am allowed to vote.
4. Until I look, I don't know what the time is.
5. Tidy up your bedroom before you get into trouble.
6. Unless you look in the cupboard, you will never find your present.
7. While the fire engines were on the way, the house burnt down.
8. Whenever I can, I go to watch Manchester United play football.
9. It often rains in November so I carry an umbrella.
10. You cannot have any sweets until you wash up.

Please note – the main clause does not always come at the beginning!

Challenge

Complete these complex sentences by adding a subordinate clause of your own.

1. P.C. Jolly arrested the man who _____.
2. Anna bought a magazine which _____.
3. I found the treasure which _____.
4. Mr Desai was a teacher who _____.
5. Tom did not get up even though _____.
6. We saw many new clothes shops when _____.
7. Mrs Smith thanked me for _____.
8. The dog went to sleep after _____.

Phrases and clauses

Look and learn

Shireen slipped over | in a muddy puddle.

clause   phrase

A **clause** may be used either as a **whole sentence** or as a **part of a sentence**. A clause always contains a **verb**.

A **phrase** does **not** contain a **verb**.
A phrase does **not make sense** on its own.

Practice

Choose a phrase from the phrase box to complete each sentence.

1. The baby chicks followed <u>behind the hen</u>_____.
2. The lion pounced, _____.
3. The man carried a bag, _____.
4. _____, it rained hard.
5. Tom did his spellings _____.
6. The alien spacecraft landed _____.
7. _____ I felt a lot better.
8. The children looked up at the _____ clouds.
9. _____ we go on holiday.
10. _____ I managed to lift the heavy rock.

Phrase Box
full of dirty washing
carelessly and untidily
After my medicine
Every summer
behind the hen
With great effort
dark, rainy
quick as a flash
During the night
on the playground

Challenge

Write if each of these is a phrase (P) or a clause (C).

1. The balloons popped. (C) 2. after the party   (__)

3. long and loud   (__) 4. They moved quietly. (__)

5. with a sigh   (__) 6. as flat as a pancake (__)

7. We skipped.   (__) 8. It rained heavily.   (__)

9. thunder and lightning (__) 10. before breakfast   (__)

11. in a while   (__) 12. The wind roared.   (__)

24

More punctuation

Look and learn

It is important to check that your punctuation is correct!

The pilot landed in his car. He drove home.

The pilot landed. In his car, he drove home.

Practice

Tick (✓) the sentences that are correctly punctuated. Cross (✗) those that are wrong.

1. After a while the car, an old wreck, rattled by. ☐
2. The boy shouted, "Please help!" ☐
3. I'm glad you came; it's been a long time. ☐
4. Leroys' pencil was broken ☐
5. Mrs Jones asked where is my bag? ☐
6. At the bottom of the sign it said: "No entry". ☐
7. The Great Plague (1665) was followed by the Great Fire (1666). ☐
8. The monster shook it's head. ☐
9. "They're not ripe yet, the gardener explained. ☐
10. The winning numbers were: 7, 42, 47 and 50. ☐
11. The boy's bikes had been stolen when they returned. ☐
12. The plane its engine in flames began to head towards the mountain. ☐

Challenge

Rewrite this passage. Punctuate it correctly.

marc and shireen decided to climb mount kilimanjaro after a while they stopped
what a marvellous view exclaimed shireen as they progressed further marcs foot
slipped he almost fell its too dangerous for me he said Im going down again

_____

_____

_____

_____

Look and learn

I did it!

admi**t**

No admittance unless accompanied by an adult

admi**tt**ance

Note – We always double the **l** in words regardless of stress e.g. marvel – marvellous, travel – travelling

When a word has one vowel before a single final consonant, double the consonant before adding a suffix – if the last syllable is stressed.

Practice

Complete this chart.

	verb	+ ing	+ ed
1.	regret	regretting	regretted
2.	occur		
3.	transmit		
4.	prefer		
5.	omit		
6.	fulfil		
7.	travel		
8.	control		
9.	cancel		
10.	quarrel		

Challenge

Choose the correct form of the word to complete each sentence.

1. Let's begin at the ___beginning___ . (begin)
2. He _____ to give me my change. (omit)
3. I am already _____ what I said. (regret)
4. The marooned pirates were _____ for help. (signal)
5. Our teacher is a very _____ person. (forbid)
6. We listened to the radio _____. (transmit)
7. The tin was wrongly _____. (label)
8. It never _____ to me to ask. (occur)
9. _____ is restricted to ticket holders. (admit)
10. The naughty child was un_____. (control)

Long and short vowels

Look and learn

wĭnd

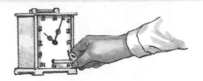

wīnd

Short vowels make the **sound** of the letter.

Long vowels say the **name** of the letter.

Practice

Show whether the vowels in these words are long ⁻ or short ˘.

1. blind   **2.** stretch   **3.** ghost   **4.** child

5. clutch   **6.** catch   **7.** rabbit   **8.** robot

9. comb   **10.** knight   **11.** halo   **12.** evil

13. rubbish   **14.** dentist   **15.** crazy   **16.** duet

17. chaos   **18.** splendid   **19.** tulip   **20.** volcano

Challenge

1. Add **le** to the end of each word. Take care. The spelling of some root words will change.

a) table____   **b)** nibble____   **c)** rip____

d) bib____   **e)** stab____   **f)** hob____

g) wig____   **h)** snug____   **i)** tit____

j) cab____   **k)** sad____   **l)** rat____

m) net____   **n)** bug____   **o)** lad____

2. Use the words you made to complete the chart.

Words containing short vowel in first syllable.	Words containing long vowel in first syllable.
nibble	table

Common word endings

Look and learn

There is a rum**our** that a creat**ure** lives in the lake.

It is helpful to learn the spelling of common word endings.

Practice

Choose either **our** or **ure** to complete each word.

1. nat _ure_
2. flav____
3. fail____
4. hum____

5. rum____
6. temperat____
7. neighb____
8. fig____

9. harb____
10. treas____
11. fut____
12. vig____

13. inj____
14. glam____
15. splend____
16. pleas____

17. vap____
18. advent____
19. mixt____
20. hon____

> Use a dictionary if you are not sure!

Challenge

Use some of the words you made to complete these definitions.

1. ____Rumour____ Something passed around as news – but may not be true.

2. _____ Strength. Energy.

3. _____ To harm oneself.

4. _____ The inability to do something.

5. _____ The taste of something.

6. _____ The time ahead.

7. _____ Steam or mist.

8. _____ Someone who lives nearby.

9. _____ A sense of fun.

10. _____ Something that has been mixed.

11. _____ Something that pleases.

12. _____ A place where ships dock.

Look and learn

machin**ery**

fact**ory**

libr**ary**

It is helpful to learn the spelling of common word endings.

Practice

Choose either **ery**, **ory** or **ary** to complete each word.

1. nurs _ery_
2. laborat_____
3. gran_____
4. fact_____
5. diction_____
6. discov_____
7. conservat_____
8. milit_____
9. brew_____
10. dormit_____
11. libr_____
12. estu_____
13. refect_____
14. bak_____
15. scen_____
16. deliv_____
17. direct_____
18. di_____
19. mock_____
20. jewell_____

> Use a dictionary if you are not sure!

Challenge

Sort the words you made into sets. Add two more words to each set.

ery words	**ory** words	**ary** words

Similes

Look and learn

A **simile** is when one thing is compared to another using the words **as** or **like**.

My tyre was **as** flat **as** a pancake.

When my mum cleans up she's **like** a whirlwind.

Practice

Match up the beginnings and endings of these common similes.

1. as tough as
2. as blind as a
3. as quiet as a
4. as busy as a
5. as green as
6. as smooth as
7. as cool as a
8. as brave as a
9. as light as a
10. as heavy as an

mouse
cucumber
grass
leather
elephant
feather
bat
silk
lion
bee

Challenge

Make up some similes of your own to finish these sentences.

1. On a stormy day the wind is like _____.
2. When Tom is happy he is like _____.
3. When Sita gets angry she is like _____.
4. The hot sun was like _____.
5. The motorbike roared past like _____.
6. When I went on the Big Dipper it felt like _____.
7. The candyfloss tasted like _____.
8. The monster hissed like _____.

Word games

Look and learn

We can learn a lot by playing **word games**. They can help us with spelling and help **improve our vocabulary**.

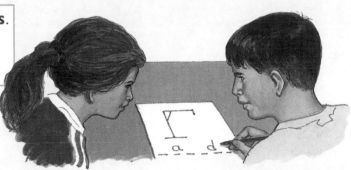

Practice

Use a dictionary to help you solve this puzzle.

1. a bubbly drink

c	h	a	m	p	a	g	n	e

2. a very prickly desert plant

c	a

3. to hold fast to

c	l

4. one hundred years

c	e

5. to get in touch with

c	o

6. a spice used to flavour food

c	i

7. a young swan

c	y

8. to bend low

c	r

9. a smooth bend

c	u

10. a hot, spicy meal

c	u

Challenge

Match up the pairs of letters in the box with the letters below to form the names of creatures.

1. **he**ron   **2.** ____mmoth   **3.** ____nx

4. ____libut   **5.** ____zzard   **6.** ____oat

7. ____ail   **8.** ____lchard   **9.** ____strel

10. ____lmon   **11.** ____eetah   **12.** ____out

he	st	qu	ke	sa	ly
tr	ch	pi	bu	ha	mu

Answers

Page 2
Practice: 1. envelope, 2. business, 3. company, 4. entrance, 5. mental, 6. photographer, 7. dictionary, 8. valuable, 9. secretary, 10. interest, 11. cemetery, 12. travel
Challenge: 1. hist<u>o</u>ry, 2. sign<u>a</u>ture, 3. Wed<u>n</u>esday, 4. sep<u>a</u>rate, 6. bach<u>e</u>lor

Page 3
Practice: 2. angle, 3. port, 4. just, 5. friend, 6. control, 7. admit, 8. magic, 9. agree, 10. sign, 11. compete, 12. propose, 13. generous, 14. suit, 15. sympathy
Challenge: answers may vary

Page 4
Practice: 1. football! 2. I hate it! 3. a marvellous invention. 4. a silver one. 5. she had pink hair. 6. Treasure Island. 7. or you'll be in trouble. 8. for painting a picture. 9. all green and slimy. 10. my old teddy.
Challenge: 1. 1666, 2. in Africa, 3. a famous composer, 4. over 26 miles, 5. a red sports car

Page 5
Practice:
1. tripped (verb), uneven (adjective), floor (noun)
2. silly, new (adjectives), boy, bike (nouns), crashed (verb)
3. old (adjective), lady, house (nouns), reached, sat (verb)
4. saw (verb), wild (adjective), horses, forest (nouns)
5. large, skilful (adjectives), cheered, scored (verbs), crowd, player (nouns)
6. giggling (adjective), girls, teacher (nouns), annoyed (verb)
7. prickly, dry (adjectives), hedgehog, leaves (nouns), snuffled (verb)
8. lazy, tall (adjectives), man, tree (nouns), was sleeping (verb)
Challenge: answers may vary

Page 6
Practice: 1. so that, 2. when, 3. who, 4. whenever, 5. in case, 6. so that, 7. as, 8. before, 9. because, 10. when
Challenge: answers may vary

Page 7
Practice: 1. bi, 2. sub, 3. aero, 4. im 5. in, 6. ir, 7. tri, 8. il, 9. pre, 10. de, 11. mis, 12. re, 13. centi, 14. anti, 15. ex
Challenge: 1. baby, 2. nasty, 3. beauty, 4. quarrel, 5. shine, 6. operate, 7. knife, 8. microscope, 9. burgle, 10. mystery, 11. attend, 12. excite

Page 8
Practice: 2. was driven (P), 3. wrote (A), 4. listened (A), 5. was won (P), 6. was chopped (P), 7. ran (A), 8. was blown (P), 9. bought (A), 10. crashed (A), 11. was scored (P), 12. chased (A)
Challenge:
2. A porter carried my luggage.
3. The cat chased the mouse.
4. The relay team won the gold medal.
5. The boy picked up the coin.
6. The girl broke the window.
7. Sam dropped the glass.
8. The horse ate the carrot.
9. The thief stole all the keys.
10. Ben's aunt hugged him.

Page 9
Practice: 1. Scarlet, 2. bracket, 3. bouquet, 4. sachet, 5. trumpet, 6. duvet, 7. cabaret, 8. ballet, 9. banquet, 10. blanket, 11. buffet, 12. ricochet
Challenge: 1. Italy, 2. Holland, 3. France, 4. Australia, 5. China, 6. America, 7. India, 8. Jamaica

Page 10
Practice: 2. separate, 3. favourite, 4. bicycle, 5. conscience, 6. piece, 7. young, 8. believe, 9. miserable, 10. weight
Challenge: answers may vary

Page 11
Practice:
1. The man asked, "Is it raining?"
2. "I've lost my pen," Rohan shouted.
3. The burglar whispered, "Someone's coming!"
4. "Where's my bag?" Mrs Shah asked.
5. You will need a pen, a ruler and some paper.
6. The noise, a loud banging noise, was awful.
7. The children's clothes were on the floor.
8. "What a lovely surprise!" the teacher said.
9. "Pass the salt, please," Sam's dad asked.
10. The boy's coat was torn.
Challenge: Danger? No. Swimming allowed!

Page 12
Practice: 2. scribble, describe, 3. vision, evident, 4. pedal, pedestrian, 5. grateful, congratulate, 6. spectator, spectacles, 7. liberty, liberal, 8. city, civilian
Challenge: answers may vary

Page 13
Practice:
1. The children began to shout when the teacher left the room.
2. Last night I read a good book when I went to bed.
3. Alexander Bell was the inventor who invented the telephone.
4. I visited Athens which is in Greece.
5. I collect stamps because they are so colourful.
6. Samuel Pepys lived in London during the Great Fire in 1666.
Challenge: answers may vary

Page 14
Practice: 1. cooks, 2. speed, 3. served, 4. never, 5. well, 6. clean, 7. nine, 8. one, 9. worm, 10. birds
Challenge:
1. has a silver lining.
2. make most noise.
3. in one basket.
4. run deep.
5. deserves another.
6. gathers no moss.
7. think alike but fools seldom differ.
8. into the fire.

Page 15
Practice: 2. umbrella, 3. confident, 4. electric, 5. infected, 6. introduce, 7. chatterbox, 8. hospital, 9. restlessness, 10. remember, 11. different, 12. January, 13. attention, 14. uniform, 15. conductor
Challenge: 2. Nov<u>e</u>mber, 3. pro<u>pos</u>al, 4. help<u>less</u>ly, help<u>full</u>y, 5. adv<u>e</u>nture, 6. lem<u>o</u>nade, 7. ex<u>cell</u>ent, 8. dis<u>a</u>ster, 9. conf<u>i</u>dent, 10. ex<u>pens</u>ive, ext<u>ens</u>ive

Page 16
Practice: 2. Beautiful, 3. Cork, 4. Dangerous, 5. Expensive, 6. Ford, 7. Glance, 8. Hexagon, 9. Icicle, 10. Jeer, 11. Knife, 12. Lance, 13. Mask, 14. Narrow, 15. Octopus , 16. Peaceful, 17. Quay, 18. Recent, 19. Scarce, 20. Till, 21. Unite, 22. Vague, 23. Witty, 24. Xmas, 25. Yacht, 26. Zoom
Challenge: 2. reservoir, 3. parliament, 4. government, 5. delicious, 6. disappear, 7. somersault, 8. altogether, 9. scissors, 10. kangaroo

Page 17
Practice: 2. believe, 3. brief, 4. chief, 5. field, 6. shield, 7. piece, 8. siege, 9. babies, 10. copies, 11. ceiling, 12. receive, 13. deceive, 14. perceive, 15. conceit
Challenge: 1. priest, 2. mischief, 3. deceit, 4. relief, 5. ceiling, 6. niece, 7. shriek, 8. sieve, 9. conceited, 10. yield, 11. receive, 12. fierce